Get ready for a
reading adventure wi[th]

™

Here's how...

Read the Page

Repeat   **Stop**

Play a Game

 Read the Whole Story →

 Play Word Hunt →

 Turn the Music On/Off →

ring!

ring!

The tin can phone was ring-ring-ringing.

"This is serious!" said Ming-Ming.

"A baby chimp!" said Turtle Tuck.

"If we don't help him, he'll be stuck!"

ring!

ring!

"He's lost in space and all alone.
We have to help him come back home!"
"But first," said Linny, "Let's get dressed,
"So that we look our very best."

BASKET

Ming-Ming made a worried face.

"We need a way to fly through space."

Linny said, "Here's what we'll do."

"We'll build a Spaceboat for our crew!"

Spaceboat

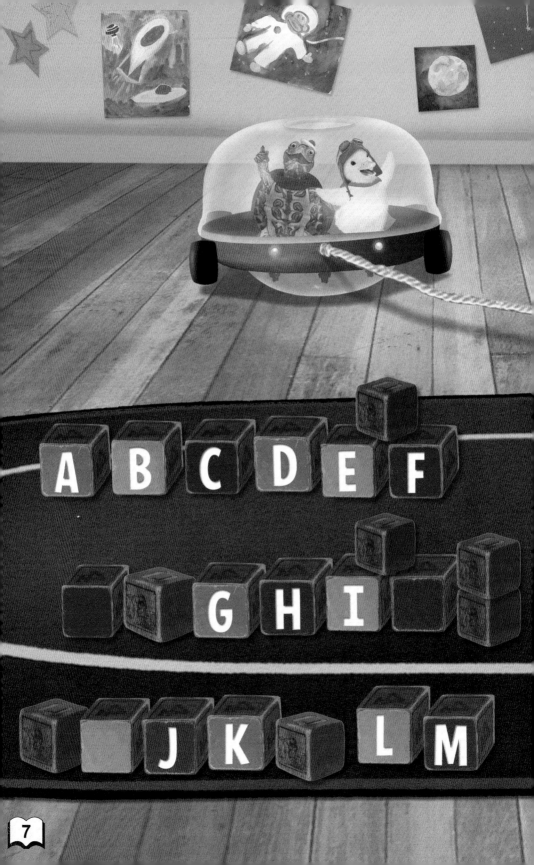

They built the Spaceboat 1, 2, 3.
Working together made it so easy.
"But wait!" said Linny. "It's too heavy."
"We'll have to tow it to get it ready."

N O P Q R

S T U V

W X Y Z

8

"Great idea!" Ming-Ming cried.

"It's time for us to take a ride!"

3, 2, 1... they blasted away.

The Wonder Pets were on their way!

Tuck shouted, "We're in space! Hooray!"
"Follow us, Baby Chimp, okay?"
Just then a meteor sped by.
That spacey rock could really fly!

12

"Oh, no!" said Tuck. "His ship won't go!"

So once again, they had to tow.

"That meteor is fast. Let's hurry!"

"I'll go!" said Ming-Ming. "Don't you worry."

They pulled and towed and flew so fast,
They got the chimp home safe at last.
His Mommy and Daddy were filled with joy
To see their little baby boy.

OSTRICH

GIRAFFE

GAZELLE

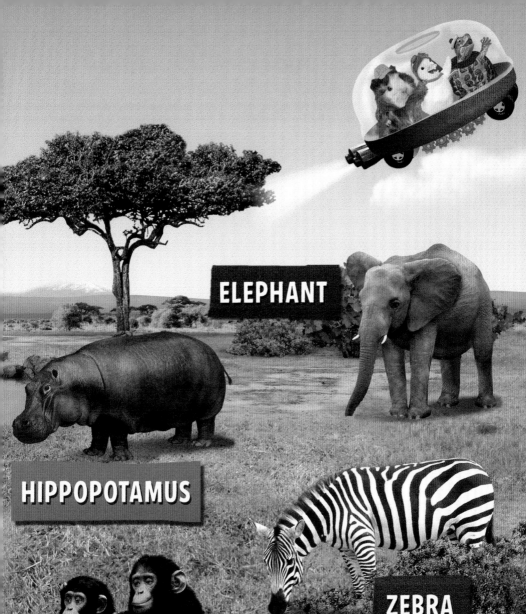

ELEPHANT

HIPPOPOTAMUS

ZEBRA

CHIMPANZEE

Now that the team is safe and sound,
Let's have some celery all around!
"Nice going, Wonder Pets! Hooray!"
It looks like teamwork saved the day!

- The End -

Classroom Rhymes

MUG

TWIG

JUG

RAT

HAT

FOX

BLOCKS

WIG